Let's Trace
Letters

ARCTURUS

ARCTURUS

This edition published in 2020 by Arcturus Publishing Limited
26/27 Bickels Yard, 151–153 Bermondsey Street,
London SE1 3HA

ISBN: 978-1-78828-121-8
CH006106NT
Supplier 29, Date 1219, Print run 9635

Illustrated by: Laura Deo
Written by: Paul Virr
Designed by: Well Nice
Edited by: Susannah Bailey

Printed in China

Writing is so much fun!
Can you write your name here?

Frakie

Note to Parents

This book will help your child to recognize and shape letters. Before they get started, you should show them how to grip a pencil close to the tip, so that they have fine control of its movement. Take a close interest in their progress and offer plenty of praise and encouragement, to show how rewarding writing can be!

One red <u>a</u>pple on the tree!

Trace the little letter "a" on the hill.

Apple pie is good to eat!

Trace the capital letter "A" on the table.

So many bright <u>b</u>right <u>b</u>alloons!

Trace the little letter "b" at the party.

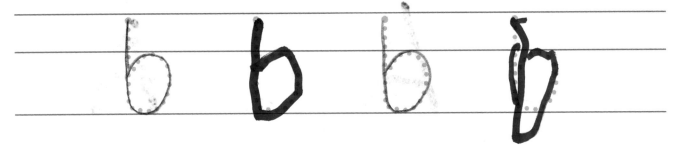

<u>B</u>ears sleep in comfy caves!

Trace the capital letter "B" on the rock.

Let's buy some yummy <u>c</u>akes!

Trace the little letter "c" on the cake!

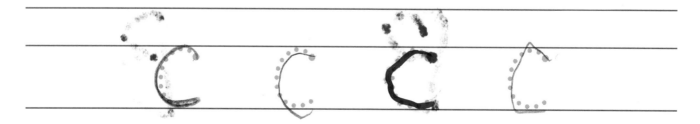

<u>C</u>ats love to curl up somewhere warm.

Trace the capital letter "C" on the rug.

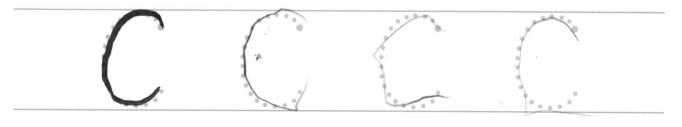

Let's <u>d</u>ance, everybody!

Trace the little letter "d" on the dance floor!

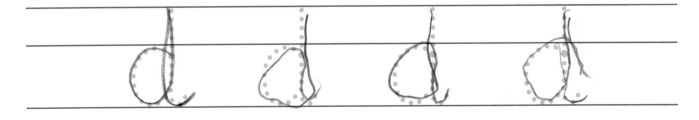

Dogs just love to dig!

Trace the capital letter "D" in the garden.

How many <u>e</u>ggs will we find?

Trace the little letter "e" in the field.

Elephants love to play!

Trace the capital letter "E" at the waterhole.

Playing with friends is fun.

Trace the little letter "f" in the bedroom.

Fish swim in the sea.

Trace the capital letter "F" under the sea.

The farmer opens the gate.

Trace the little letter "g" in the meadow.

Grandma is knitting a long scarf.

Trace the capital letter "G" on the kitchen floor.

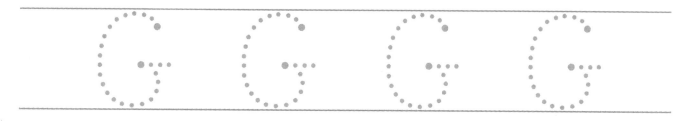

Say hello to the hippos!

Trace the little letter "h" on the water.

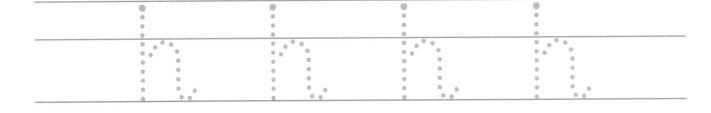

<u>H</u>orses eat hay in the stable.

Trace the capital letter "H" on the hay bale.

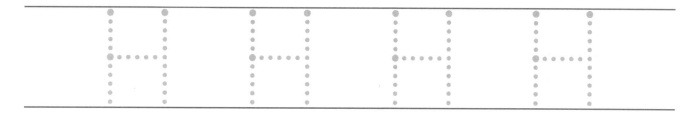

It's raining. Let's play inside today.

Trace the little letter "i" on the carpet.

Ice skating is such fun!

Trace the capital letter "I" on the ice rink.

Can you juggle too?

Jumping on a trampoline is fun!

Trace the little letter "j" and the capital letter "J" here.

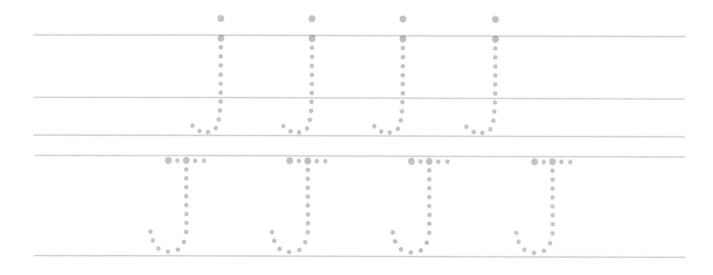

It's a lovely day to fly a <u>k</u>ite!

<u>K</u>angaroos hop to the waterhole.

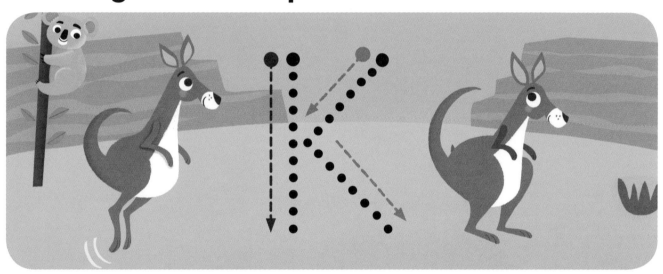

Trace the little letter "k" and the capital letter "K" here.

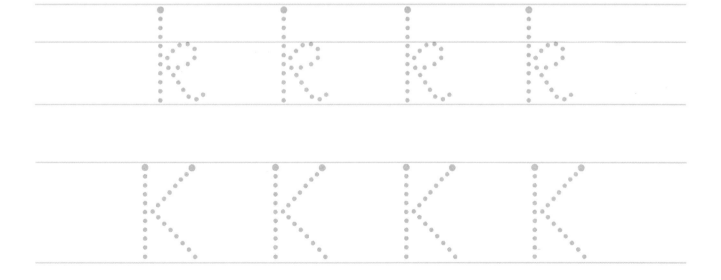

Giraffes have long necks!

Trace the little letter "l" at the zoo.

<u>L</u>ions sleep in the hot sun.

Trace the capital letter "L" in the grasslands.

The <u>m</u>oon is bright tonight!

Trace the little letter "m" on the tree.

Monkeys swing in the trees.

Trace the capital letter "M" in the jungle.

Nine tired puppies will sleep all <u>n</u>ight.

Ssshhh! Trace the little letter "n" quietly.

<u>N</u>ine noisy puppies are wide awake!

Trace the capital letter "N" now!

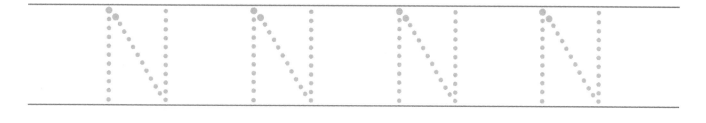

Look at the clever <u>o</u>ctopus!

Trace the little letter "o" in the sand.

<u>O</u>range juice is tasty!

Trace the capital letter "O" on the table.

Let's all play pirates!

Trace the little letter "p" on the sand.

<u>P</u>izza is great to share!

Trace the yummy capital letter "P" now!

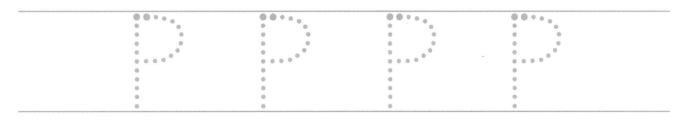

The snail is slow, but the tortoise is quick!

Quick, trace the little letter "q" on the path!

Quiet, don't wake the dragon!

Be brave and trace the capital letter "Q" on the ground.

Look at the rainbow in the sky!

Trace the little letter "r" hiding in the clouds.

<u>R</u>abbits love crunchy carrots.

Trace the capital letter "R" on the grass.

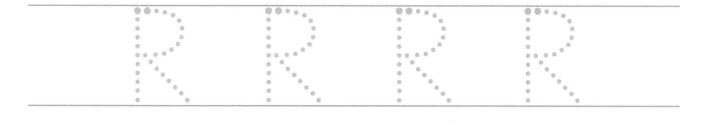

Whee! Let's go down the slide!

Trace the little letter "s" in the playground.

<u>S</u>ummer is the season for sunshine!

Trace the capital letter "S" on the beach.

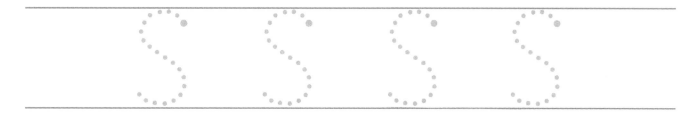

The farmer drives a green tractor.

Trace the little letter "t" in the sky.

Trucks rumble down the highway.

Trace the capital letter "T" on the road!

It's raining, but we have <u>u</u>mbrellas!

<u>U</u>nder the bridge we go!

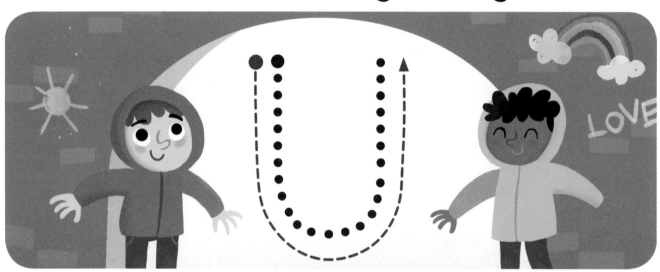

Trace the little letter "u" and capital letter "U" here.

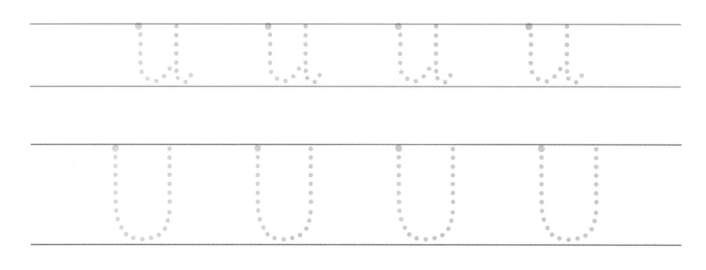

Let's put these flowers in a <u>v</u>ase.

<u>V</u>egetables are good for you!

Trace the little letter "v" and capital letter "V" here.

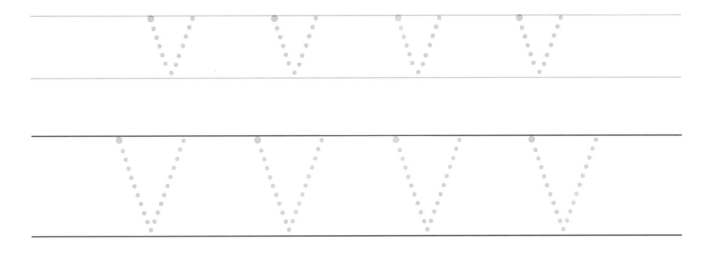

Look at the <u>w</u>ild animals!

Trace the little letter "w" hiding in the leaves.

<u>W</u>inter is a fun season.

Trace the capital letter "W" in the night sky.

I can play the xylophone!

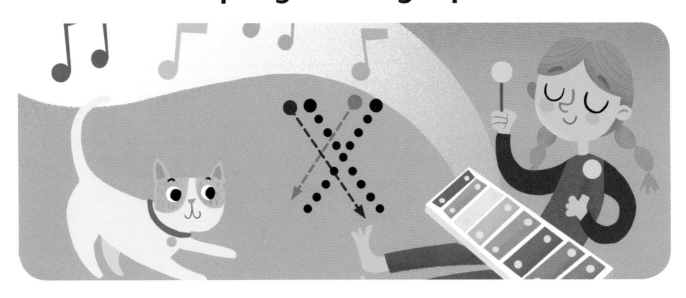

X-ray pictures look spooky!

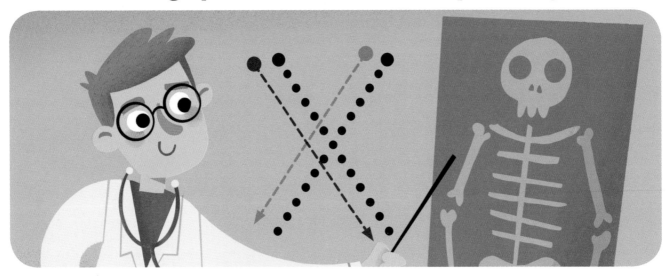

Trace the little letter "x" and capital letter "X" here.

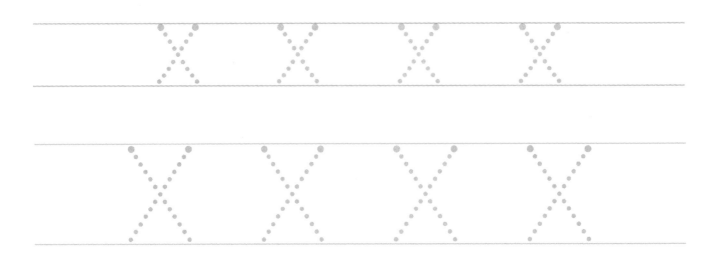

The <u>y</u>ellow speedboat is fast!

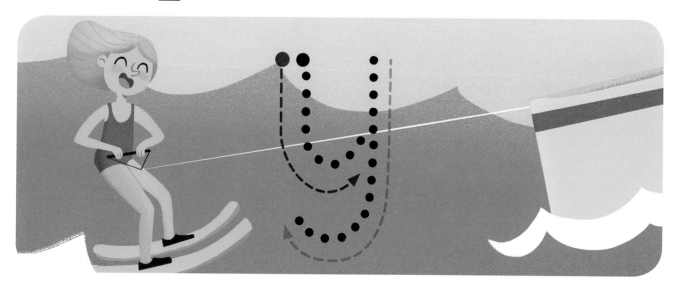

<u>Y</u>achts sail slowly across the bay.

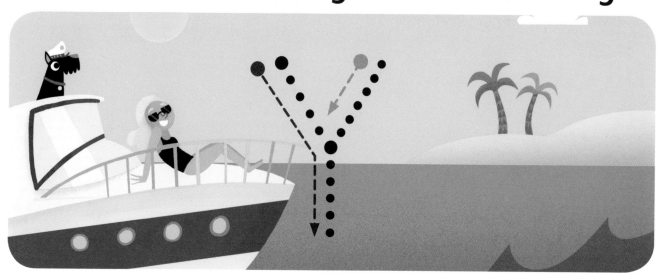

Trace the little letter "y" and capital letter "Y" here.

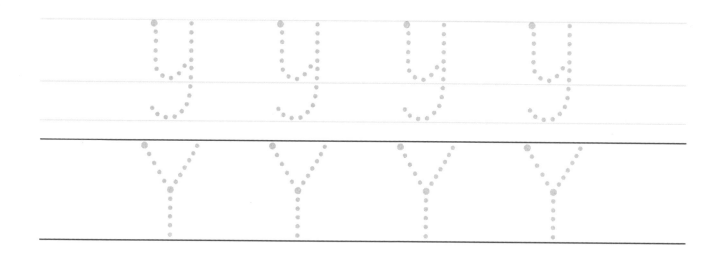

Quick, zip up your raincoats!

Zebras play on a sunny day.

Trace the little letter "z" and capital letter "Z" here.